# Bad Bitches & Power Pitches Workbook

*Precious L. Williams*

Written By: Precious L. Williams

© 2020

Published By: Pen Legacy®

Cover & Formatting By: Junnita Jackson

Edited By: U Can Mark My Word Editorial Services

Library of Congress Cataloging – in- Publication Data has been applied for.

ISBN: 978-1-7351424-1-8

PRINTED IN THE UNITED STATES OF AMERICA.

Let's face it! Your pitch is the single most important thing that could either get your business off and running or plunge your idea into the eternal depths of extinction. By definition, a "pitch" in the business world has nothing to do with delivering an amazing fastball. Instead, it describes the way presenters "throw" or provide information to prospects.

# Why Me?

Picture it! Halifax, Nova Scotia, May 2019. I just walked into St. Mary's University preparing myself to be the only African American woman to speak at the Professional Development Summit.

How did I get there? Was the audience that excited to hear from me? I was so moved I almost cried. I had not spoken internationally since 2015 and in 2017, I came within two minutes of dying. More specifically, on January 22, 2017, I attempted suicide. It's a miracle I'm even alive; my cousin found me in time and saved my life. I didn't think I would have the opportunity to speak again on ANY stage, let alone internationally.

You see, as a young girl, I was an unwanted and unloved child. No one loved me and most rejected me, but no one could take away my natural gift of speech. And this gift served me well; it provided me with a way to rise above poverty, homelessness, and despair multiple times. Throughout my life, many people have told me that I would never amount to anything, let alone become a successful serial entrepreneur. I did not come from money and did not have the right connections. Yet, like dust, I was still able to rise! The gift of speech is my claim to fame.

I thought of all this as I prepared to give my "The Art of the Killer Pitch" to the Canadian audience. To my surprise, there were over two hundred attendees who came to my session after hearing the pitch that I gave before the keynote speaker. I was told that the way I spoke, how I delivered my pitch, and the confidence I exuded had left a lasting impression on the audience. Out of 240 attendees, two hundred showed up for my presentation! Not bad for a girl from the inner city of St. Louis, Missouri.

For me, pitching is fun. It is a way of life for me, and one of the greatest moments I have ever had on stage. If you think you do not need a pitch to grow your business, or better yet, help you stand out from a crowded marketplace, you are so wrong!

Need to rise above all that is trying to hold you back? Pitching is the way forward. It will get you all the clients, customers, investors, and media you could ever want. Trust me; I know!

Now, are you ready to learn more?

# Creating the Perfect Power Pitch

Timing is everything. Keep your ideas clear, concise, and brief. A brilliant idea means nothing unless you can deliver it in a few moments of raw power. The more concise you are, the more effective you will be. It is important that you have written the content of your presentation, and also that you take the time to map out how it will be delivered. When practicing your presentation, you should attempt to replicate the actual delivery as closely as possible.

Storytelling is an essential aspect of sales pitches. It paints a picture of what life could be like with your product or service. Use your story to dramatize, build engagement, elicit emotional responses to seemingly emotionless objects, and catch your audience's attention.

Be enthusiastic. Pitching is about having the charisma, allure, and passion that will get other people excited about what you're presenting. Be cautious not to take it overboard to the point where you seem arrogant, though. A good technique for increasing your energy level is to exceed your comfort zone by about fifty percent.

Be prepared for objections. But don't take objections personal. In fact, understand that objections are usually nothing more than a mechanism that we use to get comfortable with what others are proposing before agreeing with it. When people have an interest in what you are saying, they will undoubtedly have questions. Formulating skillful and persuasive answers to these tough questions will help you demonstrate the array of abilities and traits that investors and other audiences want to see.

Offer a solution. Your product may come with many wonderful features for customers to explore. You may even want to explain and showcase all of the intricate features. However, prospects are most interested in what your product can do for them. How exactly does your product solve their biggest problems? How much money will they save by using your product? Will using your product free up their time or improve their lives for the better?

Following up is critical. Be consistent, reliable, and follow through on your word. Continue to follow up until you either get a yes or a definite no. Do not interpret a lack of response or any other kind of message as a rejection.

# Pitching Mistakes to Avoid

Did you know that you pitch daily? Don't believe me? In every conversation you have, you are pitching yourself, your vision, your thoughts, and your ideas. You are always in the mode of getting people interested in you and your life. Pitching happens naturally everywhere and every day. You just never realized its potential to help you and your business.

When it comes to pitching your business, you probably do not see the connection between your success in business and who you are as a person. Let me help you. Investors will buy you before they give money to your business. Similarly, clients and customers also buy you before they care to purchase anything from your business. Therefore, pitching is crucial and necessary. Do not underestimate how the "perfect" pitch can transform your business, life, and career.

If you have ever watched "Shark Tank," you know there is more to pitching than your name, the name of your business, and your profit margin. Investors want to know more about you and what makes you tick. From there, they can tell if you are worth the risk of their investment. There is a delicate dance to pitching. It requires dedication, focus, intensity, and energy.

I am sure you have questions; so, I will make this easy for you. You may have fears. You may not know how to present your business in a way that gets potential investors, customers, and clients excited to the point where they are ready to give you money. Trust me; I get it!

Pitching is a reality for all large, medium, and small businesses. The world is hungry for your story, your products, and your services. I know this, and I have been pitching my businesses for years with great success. It may be hard to talk about your business without getting emotional or at a loss for words, but there is a way. Let me show you how.

# What is a Pitch?

**Why do you need a pitch?**

_____

_____

_____

_____

_____

_____

_____

_____

**How long is an elevator pitch generally?**

_____

_____

_____

_____

_____

_____

_____

_____

## What can you do with your pitch?

_____

_____

_____

_____

_____

_____

_____

## Where can a pitch take you?

_____

_____

_____

_____

_____

_____

_____

_____

**Is this what you want?**

_____

_____

_____

_____

_____

_____

_____

# The Elements of a Basic Pitch

**Who are you?**

_____

_____

_____

_____

_____

_____

_____

_____

**What do you do?**

_____

_____

_____

_____

_____

_____

_____

_____

_____

**What problem(s)/challenge(s) does your product or business solve?**

_____

_____

_____

_____

_____

_____

_____

_____

**What is your specific industry? Who are your ideal clients?**

_____

_____

_____

_____

_____

_____

_____

_____

_____

**What is your BIG difference/secret sauce that your product/business offers?**

_____

_____

_____

_____

_____

_____

_____

_____

**What happens next?**

_____

_____

_____

_____

_____

_____

_____

_____

_____

Create an attention-grabbing hook or powerful call to action (CTA).

_____

_____

_____

_____

_____

_____

_____

_____

# So, What Does a Basic Pitch Look Like?

Based on what I have explained, create your basic pitch.

_____

_____

_____

_____

_____

_____

_____

_____

_____

_____

_____

_____

_____

_____

Now, try writing it 2-3 different ways.

**Option #1**

_____

_____

_____

_____

_____

_____

_____

_____

_____

_____

_____

_____

_____

_____

# Option #2

# Creating True Spark with a "Killer" Pitch

Now that you have learned the BASICS, have you:

- ❖ Practiced it out loud?
- ❖ In front of others?
- ❖ Gotten feedback?
- ❖ Do you feel more comfortable?

Good! Now, I want to introduce more advanced concepts to you to set your "killer" pitch on fire!

**READY?**

# 3 Ways to Build the Confidence to Pitch

➢ Visualize yourself as you want to be and hold that image firm. Who and what do you want to be? Be as specific as possible.

_____

_____

_____

_____

_____

_____

_____

_____

➢ Affirm yourself daily. How are you speaking to yourself? What top ten affirmations will you COMMIT to telling yourself every morning and night?

_____

_____

_____

_____

_____

_____

_____

_____

_____

➢ Do one thing that scares you every day! Continually doing this creates the momentum that can trump all FEAR! What have you been afraid to try? Write and break down your most pressing dreams and COMMIT to taking a scary step daily!

_____

_____

_____

_____

_____

_____

_____

_____

_____

_____

## IT'S TIME TO TAKE YOUR PITCH TO THE NEXT LEVEL!

Have you ever heard a pitch that took your breath away?
In this next section, I will teach you how to "kill it" in your pitches
in several unique ways. To create a "killer" pitch, start here!

# Pain Points

A great pitch starts by addressing your target market's true pain points. Knowing what truly keeps them up at night and articulating your pitch with confidence will save you time and time again. Sometimes, pain points may not be addressed because some people might not know they exist or that there is a solution.

- ❖ What is your target market struggling with in their business and/or personal life?
- ❖ How do you know?
- ❖ Have you asked them?
- ❖ Have you done your research? What research have you done? Have you gone to the library and looked up actual data? Does the data support what you want to put out to the world?
- ❖ Look at your pitch. Does it reflect what they need to hear now?
- ❖ Are you offering a real solution? If so, put it in the pitch with clarity!

# Purpose

What is the purpose of your pitch? What are you hoping to accomplish? Being very clear in your purpose can help create a great pitch.

Know why you are pitching in the first place. Why are you doing this? Why are you the ultimate resource/solution?

**Is it to:**

> Gain the first client or more clients? Why?
> Secure investor dollars? Why?
> Warm and nurture new prospects? Why?
> Become an industry leader? Why?
> Create more content that attracts your ideal audience? Why?
> Establish your expertise in the industry? Why?
> Launch new products and services that address their needs? Why?
>
> Secure paid and free speaking engagements? Why?

NOW...

Start working backward from your purpose. Begin with the end in mind.

What would you want to know about your products and services
if someone else were pitching it to you?

_____

_____

_____

_____

_____

_____

_____

_____

_____

_____

_____

_____

_____

_____

_____

_____

_____

# Know and Study Your Audience

Most entrepreneurs THINK they know who their audience is and how best to serve them. In my opinion, they are almost always WRONG! Why? Because they have not done the research or due diligence to understand their audience. This is a critical step that must be taken seriously!

Ask yourself the following questions:

- Who is your ideal target market/prospect, and why?
- What is your competitive advantage over everyone else?
- How do you measure up to what your competitors are offering?
- Are you neglecting a particular demographic?
- Are you thinking too BIG?
- Are you thinking too small?
- Why do you want to speak to this particular audience or industry?
- What is a gap not being served right now that you can exploit?
- Who was your product/service created for, and why? Does your price match who you are trying to serve? Demographics? Psychographics?

# Master Your Story

Being a master storyteller is vital in any pitch. Stories illustrate your main points as you pitch or speak. Have you ever considered what stories have defined different aspects and areas of your life?

- **What life stories make you cry?**
- **What are some of the challenges you have faced and overcome?**
- **What life experiences do you still struggle with and are making some headway on now?**
- **Which of your stories apply to your business mission and purpose? List them!**

Why are stories important in pitching? As children, we learn through hearing stories. Those stories stick with us and connect us with others. Make sure your story is emotionally compelling, relatable, and makes you appear more human and less salesy.

Some story ideas can include:

- Sharing why you started your company.
- Stating what gap(s) you saw in the market that you knew you could fill.
- Answering the question of who does your company service.
- Telling what your BIG difference/secret sauce is.

# Passion

Passion is the glue that holds your pitch together. It is the fire, energy, and intensity that will instantly attract others to you. It is your "why" taken to the next level. Express your passion every time you pitch!

Why?

- It is contagious.
- It makes others see who you really are.
- It helps you stand out.

# Your Why

Why are you doing what you are doing?

_____

_____

_____

_____

_____

_____

_____

_____

_____

_____

_____

_____

_____

_____

_____

_____

Keep asking yourself why five times in a row until you feel
the true emotion. This is more for you and not your
prospects. It keeps you in check.

# Practice Makes Perfect

Practice, practice, practice! The best pitch means nothing if it does not roll effortlessly off your tongue. That is why each of the preceding steps is important. They are the catalyst to make sure you take pitching seriously!

- **In what ways will you COMMIT to practicing your pitch?**
- **Will this be daily? If so, how many times daily?**
- **What prep work do you need to do?**
- **Who can you practice in front of who is committed to helping you get better? Why?**

# FOR SPEAKERS WHO ARE READY TO GO TO THE NEXT LEVEL!

# Speaking Gigs Galore!
# Is This Even Possible TODAY?

The truth is, you know that you have a gift and a talent for speaking. However, you are not getting any opportunities. Why is that? Why is it so hard to gain speaking gigs?

In all honesty, there are many speakers and not enough opportunities. That is why it is so important to differentiate yourself in the industry. It is not enough to want to be a motivational speaker. That was great years ago, but now, conference organizers and event planners want more than just a great, overcoming-all-odds, feel-good story. They want actionable step-by-step ways to help their audiences achieve their dreams no matter what.

What do you bring to the table that is uniquely different? Are you a refreshing, cool breeze or just offering regurgitated platitudes? People want and deserve so much more.

Have you asked yourself, "Why should they choose me?" If you can answer that, great! However, most people cannot. In fact, most people will just recite their credentials and qualifications that most speakers already have.

I propose you do an inventory of your skills, abilities, unique talents, credentials, certifications, and fun facts about yourself that stand out. Do not stop until you have over one hundred items on the list. Yes, you heard me. One hundred items at the least!

Why? Because as you're thinking about them and listing them, you will start to have more confidence in yourself. You will begin to see yourself differently. This confidence will help you start to shape your speaker pitch, which cannot be done until you do this internal inventory. So, I dare you to start now!

# The Elements of a Perfect Speech

+ Create a catchy topic.

+ Think about the mood you want your audience to experience.

+ Reflect on why your topic is timely and express it.

+ Start creating the outline.

+ Start off with a bang!

+ Reflect on how you want to start.

+ What stories illustrate your point well or speak to the overall theme of your speech?

+ Reflect on what you want your audience to do after you speak.

+ Create a powerful call to action.

+ End with fireworks!

# So, You Want to Be a Speaker... Why? Let's Be Clear, RIGHT NOW!

Why do you want to start speaking? *(This question is for amateur and novice speakers.)*

_____

_____

_____

_____

_____

_____

_____

_____

_____

_____

_____

Why did you start speaking before? (*This question is for the experienced speakers.*)

_____

_____

_____

_____

_____

_____

_____

_____

What type of speaker are you? Motivational, transformational, inspirational, educational, entertaining, etc.? Why?

_____

_____

_____

_____

_____

_____

_____

_____

_____

Are you a combination of these? If so, why?

_____

_____

_____

_____

_____

_____

_____

Who is your intended target market for speaking? Why?

_____

_____

_____

_____

_____

_____

_____

_____

_____

How does your speaking platform help others?

_____

_____

_____

_____

_____

_____

_____

Why are you committed to being the ultimate resource for your
target market?

_____

_____

_____

_____

_____

_____

_____

_____

_____

What can you speak about that is not already saturated with speakers offering their advice? *(Think long and deep about this question. This level of clarity will set you apart from your competition.)*

_____

_____

_____

_____

_____

_____

_____

_____

_____

_____

What makes you different from your competitors? Is it a real difference or a vanity/fake difference?

_____

_____

_____

_____

_____

_____

_____

_____

# Your Speaking Pitch:
# How to Differentiate Yourself
# from the Masses

## #1 Have You or Do You Have…?

> ➢ Have you surveyed the competitive landscape? If so, what are they doing that you are not doing?
> ➢ What are you doing that they are not doing?
> ➢ Compare notes to see gaps that you can exploit.
> ➢ What Are Your Signature Talks? What top three talks do you want to be known for?

   1.

_____

_____

   2.

_____

_____

   3.

_____

_____

> ➢ Why did you choose these three specifically?

- ➢ Are they in your zone of genius?
- ➢ How do you know?

## #2 What Are the Top Trending Topics in Your Industry?

- ➢ List the current top topics in your industry.
- ➢ Why do you think it is important to stay on top of what is trending in your industry?
- ➢ What Is Your Unique Selling Proposition?
- ➢ List your secret sauce.
- ➢ What do you do better than anyone else?
- ➢ Do You Have Catchy Titles and Abstracts for Your Business?
- ➢ Why is important to have a catchy title?
- ➢ What titles would make you want to check out an event?
- ➢ List Key Takeaways.
- ➢ What will your audience learn from your presentation?
- ➢ What action steps do they need to take afterwards?

# #3 Are You the Master of Your Story?

Every presentation needs a compelling story to illustrate your main points. To stand out, do the following:

- ➢ Set the scene for your audience
- ➢ Be bold and unexpected
- ➢ Know and study your audience

# #4 Can You Captivate and Titillate Your Audience?

- ➤ Grab your audience's attention in the first ten seconds of your presentation.
- ➤ Start off with a bang and end with fireworks!
- ➤ Passion changes everything.
- ➤ Challenge the status quo.

# #5 What's Your Secret Weapon?

Age, race, gender, sexual orientation, anything that society uses to make you feel bad or less than…use them to your advantage. They'll never see you coming!

- ➤ Let your perceived flaws be your secret weapons.
- ➤ How are you going to embrace your difference?
- ➤ Speak authentically.

Be yourself and be relatable. People love real people, not those who think they are perfect.

- ➤ Own your magic. Bring all of what makes you unique to the table.
- ➤ Remember, it's showtime!

# #6 Where to Look. Opportunities are Everywhere.

- ➤ Non-Profits/Foundations: Crain's (any major city)

- ➤ Colleges and Universities (schools or departments that focus on your topic)
- ➤ Conference Websites
- ➤ Mid/Medium-sized Companies/Corporations (The companies that are not in the news but are making money and feel neglected.)

# Speak Please!

## Speaking Tip #1:  Know Your Purpose

**What are you speaking about?**

_____

_____

_____

_____

_____

_____

_____

**What's your overall goal?**

_____

_____

_____

_____

_____

_____

_____

_____

_____

# Speaking Tip #2:  Focus

**What does your audience need to hear?**

_____

_____

_____

_____

_____

_____

_____

_____

# What do they want to hear?

_____

_____

_____

_____

_____

_____

_____

_____

# Speaking Tip #3:  Know and Study Your Audience

## Demographics

_____

_____

_____

_____

_____

_____

_____

_____

_____


## Psychographics

_____

_____

_____

_____

_____

_____

_____


## What do they have in common?

_____

_____

_____

_____

_____

_____

_____

_____

_____

## What are their likes?

_____

_____

_____

_____

_____

_____

_____

_____

_____

## Pet peeves?

_____

_____

_____

_____

_____

_____

_____

_____

_____

## How educated are they?

_____

_____

_____

_____

_____

_____

_____

_____

## Gender?

_____

_____

_____

_____

_____

_____

_____

_____

_____

**Finance Level?**

_____

_____

_____

_____

_____

_____

_____

**What brought them to hear you speak today?**

_____

_____

_____

_____

_____

_____

_____

_____

_____

## Speaking Tip #4: Passion Changes Everything

➤ Do not forget to show your passion for what you do.

➤ Passion is contagious!

➤ People will remember someone who loves what they do when it truly shows.

➤ Pitch, Please!

_____

_____

_____

_____

_____

# Speaking Tip #5: Powerful Call to Action

**Clearly instruct your audience to do something after your pitch.**

_____

_____

_____

_____

_____

_____

_____

_____

_____

_____

_____

_____

_____

_____

_____

_____

_____

# Securing Your Speaking **BHAG** (Big Hairy Audacious Goal)

## SPEAKING BUSINESS MODEL

- ➢ Identify Opportunities
- ➢ Create Pitch
- ➢ Ask

## COMPETITION

- ➢ Who Are You?
- ➢ What Sets You Apart?

## WHAT DO YOU WANT TO MAKE AS A SPEAKER?

_____

_____

_____

_____

_____

_____

_____

_____

_____

_____

_____

## WHAT ARE YOUR SPEAKER FINANCIAL GOALS?

_____

_____

_____

_____

_____

_____

_____

_____

_____

_____

_____

_____

_____

_____

# Competitive Intelligence

**COMPETITIVE INTELLIGENCE**

Is it necessary?

_____

_____

_____

_____

_____

_____


**COMPETITIVE INTELLIGENCE CONTINUED**

What is happening in your industry?

_____

_____

_____

_____

_____

_____

## MAJOR PLAYERS

Name the top 10 in your industry.

_____

_____

_____

_____

_____

_____

_____

_____

_____

_____

## HOT TOPICS/TRENDS

What are the most buzzed terms and topics?

_____

_____

_____

_____

_____

_____


## DIFFERENCE MAKER

What truly sets you apart?

> ➤ Credentials
> ➤ Qualifications
> ➤ Talents

_____

_____

_____

_____

_____

_____


## MAJOR ORGANIZATIONS

What major organizations and businesses should you target?

_____

_____

_____

> **Telling a story helps people get to know more about you and you become more than just a robot.**
>
> PRECIOUS WILLIAMS
> BLACKENTERPRISE.COM

# SIGNATURE TALKS

## TARGET MARKET

- ✓ Who do you want to address when speaking?
- ✓ Why?
- ✓ Are you missing a BIGGER audience?
- ✓ Are you playing too SMALL?

_____

_____

_____

_____

_____

_____

## KNOWN FOR

- ✓ What do you want to be known for?
- ✓ What topics do you love and are most knowledgeable about?
- ✓ What can you teach in your sleep?
- ✓ What topics challenge you?

_____

_____

_____

_____

_____

_____

## CONTENT CREATION

- ✓ How do you create great content?
- ✓ What is the source of your information?
- ✓ What is specifically yours that you have crafted through experience, studying, and research?
- ✓ Can you create programs, online courses, and live events of your own?

_____

_____

_____

_____

_____

_____

_____

# NETWORK

**Who is really in your network?**

_____

_____

_____

_____

_____

**Have you utilized them?**

_____

_____

_____

_____

_____

_____

_____

_____

Have you asked the heavy hitters to help you?

_____

_____

_____

_____

_____

_____

Are you a part of a great networking group?

_____

_____

_____

_____

_____

Who is helping you?

_____

_____

_____

_____

_____

_____

**Are you pitch-ready?**

_____

_____

_____

_____

_____

_____

# So, What Does a "Killer" Pitch Look Like?

KILLER Pitch Formula:
Know Story
Integrate Industry Knowledge
List skills (100+)
Life Lessons
Embrace Emotions
Repeat


Based on what I have explained, create your killer pitch.

_____

_____

_____

_____

_____

_____

_____

_____

_____

_____

_____

_____

_____

_____

_____

_____

_____

_____

Now, try writing it 2-3 different ways.

Option #1

_____

_____

_____

_____

_____

_____

_____

_____

_____

_____

_____

_____

_____

_____

_____

_____

_____

_____

Option #2

_____

_____


Now that you have learned the "Killer" Pitch system, have you:

◎      Practiced it out loud?
◎      In front of others?
◎      Gotten feedback?
◎      Do you feel more comfortable?

# Thank You from the Bottom of My Heart!

Thank you so much for purchasing this powerful book! May it speak life into your dreams and provide you with my proprietary "killer" pitch formula that will have you #bookedandbusy as executives, entrepreneurs, and speakers. You are now part of a growing worldwide movement created specifically for unapologetic, passionate, and purpose filled women pursuing their destiny. You are no longer bound by societal rules that dictate who you are and what you are truly capable of right now.

My intention in writing this book is to show you how, step-by-step, to pitch and speak your way into greatness. Nothing is impossible or out of reach for you as you go through this book. You want PAID speaking engagements? You can and will get them! You want investor dollars, mentorship, and other resources to grow and expand your company? You can and will get them! You want to attract media and get placements locally, regionally, nationally, and internationally? You can and will get these too. Let this companion workbook to the original, "Bad Bitches and Power Pitches: For Women Entrepreneurs and Speakers Only," show you the way, my bad bitches.

Take your time for greatness is on the line! Now, is not the time to play small. GO BIG!! DREAM BIG!! And most importantly, believe in yourself no matter what society, your family, friends, and/or network tell you is possible. Your dreams and vision do not need co-signors. GOD gave you your vision! 'Nuff said!

Never forget, your mess is your message. No matter what you have been through, nothing is fatal to your dreams. Rise like the phoenix you are. Give your haters a show! You have a gift! Use it BB's! With this book, BOLDLY bring forth your passion, vision, ideas, brand, book and/or business.

If you want to learn more about the Bad Bitches and Power Pitches community, we are starting a membership program just for us!! To find out more, go to my website: www.perfectpitchesbyprecious.com!

Need additional help? Whether you want to work 1 on 1 with me, or in a group program or online training? Please check out my website: www.perfectpitchesbyprecious.com and/or schedule an appointment on my calendar.

Want to share your successes with me? Contact me at personally at precious@perfectpitchesbyprecious.com

Take my FREE Bad Bitches Pitching Quiz, click on this link: www.perfectpitchesbyprecious.com/quiz

# *About the Author*

Have you ever met the full-figured diva who has taken the business world by storm and won BIG? Well now you have! Precious L. Williams, also affectionately known as the #KillerPitchMaster, can help you #slayallcompetition with her "killer" elevator pitches, media pitches, and investor pitches. Precious is a world class master communicator who works with successful entrepreneurs and speakers and helps them take their professional pitching and speaking skills to the next level. With over 25 years of experience in creating unique speaking and public speaking techniques, Williams is also known for her innovative training programs and services to her clients and sales teams at Fortune 100 companies. These companies include Google, Microsoft, LinkedIn, eBay, etc.

As a 13-time national business elevator pitch champion, Williams has been on top television shows and publications for her pitching, branding, and professional speaking skills. She was featured on Season 8 of ABC's "Shark Tank," Forbes Magazine, CNN, ABC, MSNBC, Wall Street Journal, the movie, "LEAP," as well as several others around the world. In 2019, she became a best-selling author of the #1 business book, "Bad Bitches with Power Pitches: For Women Entrepreneurs and Speakers Only" and has been featured on time square billboards, top podcasts and stages around the world.

The philosophy of her "killer" pitch is evident in the strategic and personalized creative communications and presentations solutions Williams puts forth. As serial entrepreneur, international professional speaker, and corporate trainer, Williams is equipped to bring life, authenticity, strategy, and boldness to all your oral and written communication needs.

Williams is a graduate of Spelman College and Rutgers School of Law. She currently lives in Brooklyn, New York. To learn more about Perfect Pitches by Precious, LLC, please visit: www.perfectpitchesbyprecious.com

# *Also By Precious L. Williams*

Warning! What you're about to read is a step-by-step guide to winning at the game of life. The stakes are high. So, read this only if you dare. Have you ever wondered what some women entrepreneurs and speakers do to stand out and have prospects, the media, and investors seeking them out? What's their secret sauce? How did they transcend from being average to becoming extraordinary? My dear, they are bad bitches with power pitches! A serial entrepreneur, international professional speaker, and 13-time elevator pitch champion, #KillerPitchMaster Precious L. Williams shows you how–despite growing up in poverty–she took the business, television, and media worlds by storm through the power of being a bad bitch. In her greatness, you will see yourself and learn how to unleash your bad bitch. She also shares the seven types of specific-branding bad bitches.

Through Precious's experiences, she will help you discover–or resurrect–the bad bitch inside of you. Bad Bitches with Power Pitches provides the tools of success that will have prospects seeking you out, event planners booking you for speaking engagements, and the media clamoring to get the inside scoop on you. Wherever you are in your entrepreneurial journey, this no-holds-barred, no-nonsense book will show you how to utilize your bad-bitch mentality to achieve your dreams. Dare greatly!

Available now on Amazon, Barnes N Noble, Books A Million, WalMart, and other major book retailers.

# Need Help? Work With Me

## Two Hour Laser Focused Pitch/Speaking Coaching Call with Precious

Need help with getting started with your pitch? Want tips on how to strengthen your delivery? Have questions about the Perfect Pitches by Precious method in creating the perfect pitch for you and your business? Have no fear? The #KillerPitchMaster will help you:

- ✓ Start your pitch off right
- ✓ Help you begin to create your masterpiece
- ✓ Give you at least 2 valuable tips that will help you on your pitching journey
- ✓ Answer your burning questions about pitching and presentations

## Securing Your Speaking BHAG!

Ready to finally achieve your Speaking Big Hairy Audacious Goal THIS YEAR? Although it might sound like climbing Mount Everest or one of NASA's Apollo missions, your goal is truly within reach.

As a speaker, you should be able to captivate and titillate your audience. But what is your BIG Dream? Your BHAG should be clear, compelling, and tantalizing. Speaking at TEDx, Fortune 500 companies, or on the grandest stages around the world is not a pipe dream. Our goal is to get conference and event organizers to want you to speak on their platforms. That is why this course is all about positioning you as a Speaker. Let the #KillerPitchMaster help you get your Speaking BHAG right in 2020!

Precious will show you how to set yourself up for Speaking Success in 2020 by actually achieving your BHAG Speaking Goals once and for all. Come ready to write, learn, ask questions and get moving in 2020 and beyond!

- ✓ Session #1: As a speaker, where do you most want to speak and why (your BHAG, BIG HAIRY AUDACIOUS GOAL)? Do you have a plan to get you there?
- ✓ Session #2: Do you know how to reach out to the right conference organizers and event planners to get on their radar?
- ✓ Session #3: Do you have a ready made "Speaker Pitch" that highlights why you are the right speaker for the occasion or event?"
- ✓ Session #4: Do you have a system to track your goals

## #SpeakingGigsGalore: Quickly Get Speaking Engagements in 45 Days!

Have you heard the expression, "Jack-of-all-trades, Master of none?" Most speakers and trainers fall short because they try to be all things at once. The truth is most Fortune 500 companies realize that not all their products have mass appeal. The same is also true for speakers. Determining your speaking niche is about discovering opportunities more suited to your zone of genius, expertise, market trends and the particular needs of your audience. This Masterclass, taught by Precious, is created with you in mind!

#SpeakingGigsGalore, which teaches you how to:

- ✓ Drill down and Focus on a specific, profitable speaking niche
- ✓ Design a speaker pitch that promotes and establishes you as THE authority for that niche
- ✓ How to find and pitch to KEY decision makers and organizers
- ✓ How to Write articles/blogs for Niche Publications, helping you stand out
- ✓ Develop a long term speaking plan and stick with it
- ✓ And So Much More!

## The Killer Pitch: RockstarConfidence

Have you ever met a real life rockstar or even seen one on stage? If so, you may have found yourself feeling their energy, appreciating their presence or even perhaps saying to yourself, "Wow," I want to be like that." Trust me, no drummer, guitarist, or even vocalist had instant success or #RockstarConfidence. They all had someone to nudge them in the right direction, be it a mentor or a coach.

It takes that same type of confidence to get TOP media attention so that you can market your products, services, books and programs to their audience. So if you are looking for that special someone who is going to help bring that #RockstarConfidence sales rhythm out of you, look no further than this course!

The #KillerPitchMaster will give you the confidence of a rockstar to attract media to you and get them to feature you time and time again. In this training, you will learn firsthand

- ✓ How to do a media pitch.
- ✓ Build the buzz around your brand that will make it more marketable.
- ✓ The specific steps to go after the media you want to be placed in.
- ✓ The exact places you should be to get noticed by your selected media outlet.
- ✓ And how to stamp that rockstar swag that will make you stand out against your competitors.

## The "Killer" Pitch: An Introduction

You have a great idea and are starting to see some traction! You created a business, have all the proper documentation, and a cool new website. Crickets?!? Now what? No one is lining up to buy your products, you have little to no clients and you are starting to feel like a failure. What went wrong? Can this be fixed? Yes!

My friend, you forgot an important lesson! You MUST attract and engage your audience through the power of a killer pitch. But how do you get started? To whom do you pitch successfully? This course, The Killer Pitch: An Introduction, is for those new to the pitching game and want to hit the ground running and succeed. Through this 6 week, 1 hour modules, biweekly coaching sessions + homework, you will learn:

- ✓ Perfect Pitch 101: The Basics
- ✓ Perfect Pitch 102: Who is the Perfect Target Market for My Business?
- ✓ Perfect Pitch 103: Creating the Perfect Pitch for Your Target Market
- ✓ Perfect Pitch 104: Addressing Their Pain Points and Objections
- ✓ Perfect Pitch 105: Standing Out from Your Competition
- ✓ Perfect Pitch 106: How to Ensure They Choose You and BUY NOW!!!

CPSIA information can be obtained
at www.ICGtesting.com
Printed in the USA
FSHW020110151020
74737FS